In Heart and Home

Books in this series—

After God's Heart:
A Woman's Workshop on First Samuel
Behold Your God:
A Woman's Workshop on the Attributes of God
Growing Godly:
A Woman's Workshop on Bible Women
New Life:
A Woman's Workshop on Salvation
Our Life Together:
A Woman's Workshop on Fellowship
Walking in Wisdom:
A Woman's Workshop on Eccelesiastes
A Woman's Workshop on the Beatitudes
A Woman's Workshop on Bible Marriages
A Woman's Workshop on David and His Psalms
A Woman's Workshop on Faith
A Woman's Workshop on Forgiveness
A Woman's Workshop on James
A Woman's Workshop on Mastering Motherhood
A Woman's Workshop on Philippians
A Woman's Workshop on Proverbs
A Woman's Workshop on Romans
A Life Styled by God:
A Woman's Workshop on Spiritual Discipline for Weight Control
People in Turmoil:
A Woman's Workshop on First Corinthians
Designed by God:
A Woman's Workshop on Wholeness
Spread the Word:
A Woman's Workshop on Luke
In Heart and Home
A Woman's Workshop on Worship

In Heart and Home

A Woman's Workshop on Worship

With Helps for Leaders

Robert E. Webber

Grand Rapids, Michigan
Zondervan Publishing House

In Heart and Home: A Woman's Workshop on Worship

This is a Lamplighter Book
Published by the Zondervan Publishing House
1415 Lake Drive, S.E., Grand Rapids, Michigan 49506

Library of Congress Cataloging in Publication Data

Webber, Robert
In heart and home.
1. God—Worship and love. 2. Public worship. 3. Women—Religious life. I. Title.
BV4817.W38 1984 248.3 84-21030
ISBN 0-310-36681-X

Edited by Janet Kobobel

Printed in the United States of America

85 86 87 88 89 90 / 10 9 8 7 6 5 4 3 2 1

CONTENTS

WHY A WORKSHOP ON WORSHIP?

In the early part of the 1970s, I began to realize how little I knew about the subject of worship.

For most people, that probably would not be a startling discovery. But for me it was different; I was a graduate of a Christian college and held degrees from three different seminaries. Yet in all of those years of education, I had never had a course on worship. And no one, either in seminary or in the local church, had given me any guidance in the subject.

So I began to observe patterns of worship. I began to ask questions like, "Why do you do what you do?" To my dismay, I discovered that most people (including ministers) really did not have a good grasp on the "why" of worship. Neither did I.

Next I went to the library and discovered that there were scores of books written on the subject. As I read about the biblical basis of worship, the experience of the church at worship, and the contemporary need to spend more time in worship, a new world opened up to me.

I invited some of my students to join me in a journey into worship; in a course that I titled "The History and Theology of Worship," we read, discussed, visited worshiping communities, and grew together.

In recent years, many others have gone through an experience similar to mine. It now seems that there are pockets of people in every congregation that are asking important questions about worship.

Worship begins in the heart and the home and then extends into the church and the world. For this reason, it is important for women who play a major role in shaping the family worship experience to understand the meaning of worship.

Consequently, I have three purposes in mind in structuring and developing this workshop.

First, it is important that worship be understood. Worship is not something done haphazardly, nor is it to be entered into lightly. God made us to worship Him and to bring Him glory. Our concern then is to understand worship more fully and to learn how to more completely fulfill our calling to worship God.

A second purpose of this workshop is to assist you in the practice of worship. Worship is not merely a matter of the mind, but a matter of the heart and body as well. Our calling is to be a worshiping person, a worshiping family, a worshiping congregation. Thus, this workshop intends to increase your actual practice of worship.

And finally, this workshop intends to help you become a change-agent. If you understand more about worship and if you put worship into practice in your home, your interest in worshiping will spill over into your local church. This may be more indirect than direct, depending on the role you play in the determination of worship in your local congregation. Nevertheless, it is my concern and prayer that you lead others into a richer understanding and a more fulfilling experience of worship.

HOW TO BE A GOOD PARTICIPANT

In Heart and Home is designed for group use. While it is possible to do this study alone, it will be much more rewarding to do it in a group.

In group situations, we learn from each other. To help you contribute to the group process of learning, here are a few things to keep in mind.

Prepare

1. Set aside time for study.

It's always best to set aside a specific study time. Treat this time as taken; only an emergency can budge you from this commitment. You might want to set aside three specific half-hour periods during the week.

Each study is divided into three parts: (1) the biblical basis; (2) the experience of the church; and (3) the practical implications for today. Take your time to work through and meditate on each section.

2. Begin with prayer.

Always ask the Holy Spirit to give you an open and sensitive heart and a clear head.

3. Mark your Bible.

Use a Bible that you can mark. As you answer the questions, underline those Scripture portions that are especially meaningful to you.

4. Think of concrete examples.

Ideas and abstract thinking have their place. However, in a study of this kind, you will want to think of instances from your own experience and that of others that will illustrate your thoughts.

5. Follow the rules of etiquette.

It's always helpful to yourself and to the group to be on time, to bring your Bible, and your book *In Heart and Home*.

Participate

1. Remember, there is no such thing as a stupid question.

I tell my students, "If a question comes to mind, it's a valid issue for you." When that question arises out of your concern to understand, it needs to be stated. Ask it!

2. Share yourself.

The purpose of a workshop is to get to the nitty-gritty. Ideas and abstract opinions are sometimes in order. But in a discussion of this nature, you will want to think in concrete terms. Therefore, speak out of your own experience. Share something of yourself as you explain an idea or recount an occurrence that helped to shape your life and spiritual well-being.

Try to ask questions of each other that elicit examples and illustrations. Ask, "How have you experienced this?" and "What difference does this make in your life?" and "Here is my situation; what do you think I should do?"

Apply

1. Set aside time for personal worship.

Since one purpose of this course is to worship, it would be good to set aside some time each day for personal prayer and meditation.

2. Establish family worship.

Go to your local bookstore and buy a book to help you in family worship. If you put into practice the principles you are learning in this study, the rewards will be significant.

3. Get involved in the worship committee of your church.

Much of what you will study in this workshop relates to what you do on Sunday morning. You may find yourself eagerly longing to do something about or for morning worship. Ask your pastor to put you on the worship committee or to involve you in morning worship.

4. Determine to live a life of service.

Worship relates to our life in the world. It has to do with our work, with our treatment of loved ones and neighbors. Ask, "What specific thing can I do this week to worship God through my service in the world?"

HELP FOR THE TEACHER

Now that you've accepted the responsibility to direct this workshop on worship, you may be asking yourself, "Why did I ever agree to do this?"; "How will I ever teach this material?"; and "Will we benefit from the study?"

These are natural questions. And being a little nervous is not only normal but also good. I've been teaching since 1960, yet every time I face a new class of students, I experience some nervousness. But I've found that students are people like myself. Once the class has started, and we've gotten to know each other, I become much more relaxed. We usually end up having a fun time as we learn. The same will probably happen in your group.

Methods of Teaching

There are, of course, different ways of teaching and learning. In classroom situations, most of us have been taught through the lecture method. But some subjects are more quickly understood through field experience. And some topics are best addressed through discussion and the exchange of ideas. This course has been designed to employ both field experience and discussion.

Field experience is used because worship is not something that we simply talk about but something that we do. Therefore, encourage each member of the group to have family devotions. This will help each person put the principles of worship into practice.

The members of your group may find that worshiping in the home will be the most exciting dimension of this study. It will give you a common task as well as a common experience to discuss. And comparing successes and failures in home worship will produce a sense of excitement and camaraderie among the families. At some point in your study, you may want to include all the families for a dinner and a worship service.

The workbook itself is designed to help you ask provocative questions and to stimulate interesting discussion. In this part of your workshop experience, you don't want to give answers or lecture. Rather, you'll want to *guide* a discussion that moves easily from the biblical basis, through the historical experience of the church, and into practical application.

The Biblical, Historical, and the Practical

As you prepare, pay special attention to the threefold development of each chapter. There is an internal progression built into each session that will keep you from wandering.

In teaching, I've always found it helpful to begin with the Bible. Since Scripture is the source of our knowledge and the ultimate authority for the Christian, it's natural to ask, "What does the Bible say about this?"

Second, I take my students into the history of the church. Because Christians throughout history have always taken the Bible seriously, they too have asked, "What does the Bible say?" The answers and experiences which have been given to them by the Holy Spirit are highly pertinent and valuable for us today. We don't have to simply repeat what they have done, but we can and ought to learn from their example.

Finally, then, I bring the students to the present time and place. At this point each must ask, "How can worship come alive for me today?" When you come to the application part of your study, be sure to bring the knowledge which you have gained from the biblical and historical inquiry into focus. When the practical question is asked within the context of understanding, extreme opinions can be avoided, and helpful suggestions and directions will be made.

Fielding Discussion

Since the bulk of your time will be spent in discussion, it's a good idea to review basic rules for conducting a good discussion. Remember to:

1. Ask only one question at a time.

Make sure your question is singular. It's confusing to cluster a group of questions together. Instead, have a clear focus to your question so that it can be easily understood.

2. Wait for a response.

It may feel awkward not to have an immediate response to your question. But remember, time is needed to assimilate the question and to think about it. If you ask another question on top of it, or say something for filler, you'll disrupt the thinking process.

3. Ask if someone wishes to respond to the response.

It is not necessary for the teacher to respond to every answer. Much more interaction takes place if as many other people are involved as possible. You might say, "Joan, how do you respond to Mary's answer?" or "Does anyone else have a similar response?" or "Does someone see it differently from Mary?" or "Let's get a different perspective. What do you think, Helen?"

4. Acknowledge a good answer.

Whenever a clear and concise answer is given to a problem, make sure you recognize its value. You may say, "That's really to the point," or "I find that to be helpful because . . ." or "What I like about your answer is . . ."

5. Avoid the "yes . . . but" approach.

If the answer isn't what you are looking for, don't put down the student by saying, "That's wrong," or "I don't think you understand the issue." Instead say, "Let's get some more responses." Then, when a response is more to the point, build on that answer, and affirm its correctness.

6. Stick to the subject.

In a discussion it's easy to go off on a tangent. Sometimes it's good and helpful to follow a tangential issue, but usually it's not. Handle a tangent by saying, "That's a really good issue that we might discuss during our break," or "Is there a way that that issue can actually lead us back into our major concern for today?"

7. Relax!

The group is in this together, and each person has become involved so she can learn more about worship—including you. You don't have to be the authority or to know all the answers. Your role is simply to guide the group.

1

WORSHIP IS SOMETHING WE DO

I once heard a choir director jokingly say to a congregation, "In heaven our pastor is going to be without a job, but mine will continue. Preaching will come to an end, but worship and singing will never cease." There were a few "Amens" (one from the pastor), after which the choir director reminded the choir members that practice for heavenly worship begins on earth.

He expressed a good point. In heaven we will no longer be kept busy with house chores, schedules, errands, and the numerous things that occupy our waking moments. In heaven we will be about the business of worship.

But worship is also an indispensable part of our Christian faith in the here and now. Yet too little seems to be said and done about worship. We concern ourselves with purity of thought, positive behavior patterns, missions, and fellowship, but very little instruction is given on how to worship. That makes our study an imperative. It is our purpose to find out what worship is in the heart, the home, the church, and the world, and then to do it!

To begin, we should understand that worship is not something done to us or for us. Rather, worship is something done by us. In this sense, worship is a verb. It is something we do.

The Biblical Basis

Students of theology recognize that God is known to us in His being and in His actions. Interestingly, worship acknowledges the same distinction. We worship God for who He is, and we worship God for what He has done. The following Scriptures will help us come to grips with this twofold emphasis of worship.

We worship God for who He is.

1. Read Genesis 28:10–22.

   a. What is the vision of God and the response of Jacob expressed in this passage? ____________________

   ____

   ____

   b. Compare Jacob's vision with that of St. John by reading Revelation 4:1–11. What do you sense about God from Jacob's vision? From John's? ______________

   ____

   ____

   ____

2. Read Exodus 34:29–35.

a. What does this passage suggest should happen in our worship experience today? ______________________

____

b. How can we express the awesome experience of being in the presence of God in our worship today? __

____

____

____

3. Read Romans 11:33–36.

a. Rewrite this passage in your own words. __________

____

____

____

____

____

____

____

b. What kind of an attitude toward God does this passage stimulate in you? ______________________

____

____

____

____

____

We worship God for what He has done.

4. Read Exodus 20:8–11.

   a. What is the reason given for worship in this passage? __

   ____

   b. Compare Exodus 20:8–11 with Revelation 4:11. In what specific ways can you worship God for creation?

   ____

   ____

   ____

5. Read Deuteronomy 5:12–15.

   a. What is the reason given for worship in this passage? __

   ____

   b. Compare Deuteronomy 5:12–15 with Revelation 5:9. In what specific ways can you worship God for redemption? ____________________

   ____

   ____

   ____

6. Read Deuteronomy 6:6–9.

   a. How does this passage relate to worship? __________

   ____

   ____

   b. Compare Deuteronomy 6:6–9 with 1 Peter 2:9. What is the calling of the church? ________________

   ____

   ____

____

____

The Experience of the Church

One of the major ways the church has worshiped throughout history is with its hymnology. In the hymns of the church, God is worshiped both for His character and for His actions. The following hymns illustrate this principle. Meditate on them, and learn to be attentive to the content of the hymns you sing in church. Your meditation can be a way of offering praise and thanks to God.

7. A hymn praising God in His character:

> Holy, Holy, Holy! Lord God Almighty!
> Early in the morning our song shall rise to thee:
> Holy, Holy, Holy! merciful and mighty,
> God in three Persons, blessed Trinity.
>
> Holy, Holy, Holy! all the saints adore thee,
> Casting down their golden crowns around the glassy sea;
> Cherubim and seraphim falling down before thee,
> Which wert, and art, and evermore shalt be.
>
> Holy, Holy, Holy! though the darkness hide thee,
> Though the eye of sinful man thy glory may not see,
> Only thou art holy; there is none beside thee,
> Perfect in power, in love, and purity.
>
> Holy, Holy, Holy! Lord God Almighty!
> All thy works shall praise thy Name, in earth, and sky, and sea;
> Holy, Holy, Holy! merciful and mighty,
> God in three Persons, blessed Trinity. Amen.
>
> Reginald Heber, 1827

What does this hymn say about the character of God? ___

____

____

____

____

____

8. A hymn that extols God for His mighty works:

Crown him with many crowns,
  The Lamb upon his throne;
Hark! how the heavenly anthem drowns
  All music but its own:
Awake, my soul, and sing
  Of him who died for thee,
And hail him as thy matchless King
  Through all eternity.

Crown him the Son of God
  Before the worlds began,
And ye, who tread where he hath trod,
  Crown him the Son of man;
Who every grief hath known
  That wrings the human breast,
And takes and bears them for his own,
  That all in him may rest.

Crown him the Lord of life,
  Who triumphed o'er the grave,
And rose victorious in the strife
  For those he came to save;
His glories now we sing
  Who died, and rose on high,
Who died, eternal life to bring,
  And lives that death may die.

Crown him of lords the Lord,
  Who over all doth reign,
Who once on earth, the incarnate Word,
  For ransomed sinners slain,

Now lives in realms of light,
  Where saints with angels sing
Their songs before him day and night,
  Their God, Redeemer, King.

Crown him the Lord of heaven,
  Enthroned in worlds above;
Crown him the King, to whom is given
  The wondrous name of Love.
Crown him with many crowns,
  As thrones before him fall,
Crown him, ye kings, with many crowns,
  For he is King of all.

Matthew Bridges, 1851

List and meditate on the works of God that this hymn celebrates. ____________________

____

____

____

____

Practical Implications for Today

9. Worship in the heart. Read Daniel 3:8–16. What does this passage have to say about the resolves we need to make in our hearts? Have you made any resolves about worship? What resolves do you need to make? ________

____

____

____

____

10. Worship in the home. Read Romans 10:14–15. What can we do in home worship to tell and act out the story of who God is and what He has done? State at least one specific idea that has worked in your home. Think of one idea you would like to try. ______________________

11. Worship in the church. Read Revelation 19:1. Be aware of how you worship God in your church service this Sunday. Write down the ways in which you worship God for who He is: ______________________

    for what He has done: ______________________

12. Worship in the world. Read Acts 1:8. How has your worship of God affected your life? In what way(s) can your actions express who God is and what He has done?

2

WORSHIP IN THE HEART

Worship is both internal and external. It is something that occurs within the heart and through the actions that flow from the heart.

Consequently, true worship presupposes an internal experience of God and an external expression of that experience. He who was born in Bethlehem must also be born in our hearts. He who walked the roads and paths of Palestine must also walk in the streets of our world through us. He who died on the cross must take us into His death. He who rose again for our salvation must bring us into a participation with Him in His resurrection. And He who sent the Holy Spirit must give us the Holy Spirit to dwell in our lives.

True worship begins in the heart where the meaning of Christ's birth, life, death, and resurrection finds seed. It proceeds into the home as the most immediate context in which faith is lived out. From there, worship finds expression in the corporate worship of the church, that community of believers gathered in the name of Christ, and is finally culminated in the service that the Christian offers to the world.

In this study we will focus on the first of those places where we worship—in the heart.

The Biblical Basis

In this world there are many kinds of spirits that dominate and seek to control our lives. A few of these spirits include:

The spirit of independence and autonomy
The spirit of cynicism
The spirit of consumerism
The spirit of materialism

As you ready yourself to worship, it seems good and proper to test your own life attitude against that of the spirit which is required for true worship. The following Scriptures will help you discover that spirit.

1. Read Job 38:1–12. Remember how everything had been taken away from Job to test his faithfulness to God? At this point he is angry and doubts God's wisdom.

   a. What is the meaning of God's question in verse 2? ____

   ____

   ____

   b. Why is God asking Job all these questions? ________

   ____

   ____

2. Read Job 42:1–6.

a. What is Job's answer to God's questions? ______

______

______

b. What attitude does his answer show? ______

______

______

c. What connection does that attitude have with worship? ______

______

______

d. Do you think Job is too extreme in his view? ______

______

______

3. Read Luke 1:46–55. These are the words of the Magnificat that were said by Mary in celebration of the coming of the Messiah.

   a. What is Mary's attitude? Write down the words and phrases that capture her posture before the Lord. ______

   ______

   ______

   ______

   b. What can you discern about God's view toward the poor and rich from the Magnificat? Write down specific words and phrases that give you that understanding. ______

____

____

4. Read Matthew 11:28–29. These famous words of invitation were spoken by Jesus to the poor and needy of Palestine.

   a. What do these words presuppose about the attitude of the one coming to Jesus? ____________________

   ____

   ____

   b. What does this invitation reveal about the character of Jesus? ______________________________

   ____

   ____

   c. What do these words suggest about the heart attitude of the person who would worship Jesus today? ________

   ____

   ____

5. Read Philippians 2:5–6:8.

   a. Describe Jesus' attitude in your own words. __________

   ____

   ____

   b. What steps does a person need to take to have that attitude? ______________________________

   ____

   ____

c. How will such a mindset prepare us to truly worship? _

___

___

The Experience of the Church

6. Here is a statement by John Chrysostom, Bishop of the church in Constantinople in A.D. 380:

   "No matter where we happen to be, by prayer we can set up an altar to God in our heart."

   This statement tells us several things about worship. List three. ___

   ___

   ___

   ___

7. St. Augustine's prayer book contains selections for confession and preparation of the heart for true worship. Here is a step-by-step exercise for self-examination. Do it prayerfully. (Adapted from *St. Augustine's Prayer Book*, ed. Loren Gavitt [New York: Holy Cross Publications, 1974], pp. 111–138.)

   Think of yourself as God's child and of the wickedness of following Satan rather than your loving Father.

   Read the following descriptions of various types of sins, and write down what you remember of your sins. If there are any of the descriptions you don't understand, leave them unanswered.

   Don't be in a hurry, and don't vex yourself because you can't remember all your sins. Be honest with God and with yourself; this is all God asks of you.

Don't fret about your sins. Remember, you are trying to recall them in order that you may be forgiven, not that you may be condemned: "A broken and a contrite heart, O God, thou wilt not despise" (KJV).

a. *Presumption*. Dependence on self rather than on God. Satisfaction over our spiritual achievements. Preference for our own ideas, customs, schemes, or techniques. Unwillingness to surrender to and abide in Christ. ______________________________

____

____

____

b. *Vanity*. Boasting, exaggerating, drawing attention to ourselves by talking too much, by claiming ability, wisdom, experience, or influence we do not have, or by eccentric or ostentatious behavior. Undue concern over money or too much energy expended on looks, dress, surroundings, etc., in order to impress others; or deliberate slovenliness for the same purpose. Seeking, desiring, or relishing flattery or compliments. __________

____

____

____

c. *Malice*. Ill-will, false accusations, slander, backbiting. Reading false motives into others' behavior. Initiation, collection, or retailing of gossip. Arousing, fostering, or organizing antagonism against others. Unnecessary criticism, even when true. Deliberate annoyance of others, teasing, or bullying. ______________________

____

____

____

d. *Covetousness.* The refusal to respect the integrity of other creatures, expressed in the inordinate accumulation of material things; in the use of other persons for our personal advantage; or in the quest for status, power, or security at their expense. ______________

____

____

____

8. The Jesus Prayer. A traditional prayer from the early church that is still used today by countless Christians is the Jesus Prayer. It is a simple but exceedingly profound prayer:

   Lord Jesus Christ, Son of God,
   have mercy upon me a sinner.

   Read the following comment on the Jesus Prayer written by Per-Olof Sjogren and consider the full meaning of this brief prayer as he explains it.

   > The Jesus Prayer is something of a song of praise, an act of worship, a thanksgiving that there is this Jesus-way to the heart of God, and that we are allowed to tread this way. It is one way to obey the Commandment about "the name of the Lord your God"; it is an extension of the first petition in the Lord's prayer: "Hallowed be thy Name." It is a summary of the whole gospel: God sent his Son to be a redemption for the sins of men. He let him die and rise again so that today he lives and reigns eternally as Lord over the living and the dead. If we go through the Creed attentively and thoughtfully, we find a summary of the whole content of the Bible. Similarly

> those who pray the Jesus Prayer thoughtfully find the same: Lord Jesus Christ, Son of God, have mercy upon me. Every word is heavy with meaning, every word gives the richest associations to those who know their Bible. Besides being a direct prayer to Jesus it contains also teaching about him, about his work of redemption, his dignity as king, his deity, and his loving mercy. (*The Jesus Prayer* [Philadelphia: Fortress Press, 1975].)

Now, meditate on the prayer. Turn it over in your heart and let it speak to you. Write your response in the space below. ____________________________________

____

____

____

____

Practical Implications for Today

9. Worship in the heart. Read Romans 10:9–10. What does your heart tell you about your personal relationship to God through Jesus Christ? In what situations have you publically confessed Christ as Lord? ____________________

____

____

____

____

10. Worship in the home. Read Matthew 6:19–21. How do these verses help you to think concretely about your home life? According to your self-evaluation, where is your heart in your home life? Write down specific

illustrations of where your heart is and any resolves to change you need to make.

illustrations: ______________________________

____

____

____

resolves: ______________________________

____

____

____

11. Worship in the church. Read Hebrews 10:19–25. State at least four ideas from this text which will help you worship in the church more fully.

    a.

    b.

    c.

    d.

12. Worship in the world. Read 2 Corinthians 3:1–3. How does this passage emphasize worship in the world? What are you doing now that makes you an epistle? What can you do for others that will make your life a more significant epistle of Jesus Christ? ______________________________

____

____

____

____

3

WORSHIP IN THE HOME

Home, we are told, is the place where we are free to be ourselves. I suppose all of us can say "Amen" to that.

Most of us find that when we are at work, in church, or in a public setting, we are usually a bit more guarded. Maybe we protect ourselves from being fully known to avoid a challenge or embarrassment.

But home is the place where the real "me" is most evident. We are among those who love us most, where commitment runs deep, where toleration of our idiosyncrasies is frequently at its highest level.

Perhaps because home is the place where we are most free to just relax, it is also the place where it is most difficult to worship. Yet the home is a crucial setting in which to witness to our faith, to express our relationship to God, and to demonstrate the power of His Word in our lives.

In this lesson, we will look at worship in the home to learn how to enrich our own home worship.

The Biblical Basis

The earliest Christians brought their Jewish heritage with them to their new faith. One of their traditions was home worship. Consequently, a logical place to begin studying home worship is in the Old Testament.

1. Read Deuteronomy 6:6–9.

   a. What are the words and commands that are to be taught? See Deuteronomy 5. ____________________

   ____

   ____

   b. What approach to teaching and worship in the home does this passage imply? ____________________

   ____

   ____

   c. What do you think is the meaning of "hands," "eyes," "doorposts," and "gates" in verses 8–9?

   Hands ______________________________

   Eyes ______________________________

   Doorposts ___________________________

   Gates ______________________________

2. Read Deuteronomy 6:20–25. What does this passage reveal about how truth is passed down within the home?

   ____

   ____

____

____

3. Read Proverbs 9:1–12.

   a. What is the central thrust of verses 1–6? __________

   ____

   ____

   b. What is the major emphasis of verses 7–9? ________

   ____

   ____

   c. What do you think is the key idea of verses 10–12? __

   ____

   ____

   d. Develop three principles for home worship from these three sections of Proverbs 9:1–12. ____________

   (1) ____________________________________

   (2) ____________________________________

   (3) ____________________________________

In the New Testament, the home is also seen as the center for faith and worship. In the home, faith is established, nourished, and passed down. Read, study, and meditate on the following New Testament examples.

4. Read Luke 2:41–52.

   What does this passage say about worship in the home of Joseph and Mary and the training Jesus received in His human home? ________________________

   ____

____

____

5. Read Luke 10:38–42.

   What do these verses say to us about our home as a place of worship? ______________________

   ____

   ____

   ____

   ____

6. Read 2 Timothy 1:5.

   What does this verse imply about the role of women in shaping spiritual understanding and Christian character in the home? ______________________

   ____

   ____

   ____

   ____

The Experience of the Church

7. The reading below describes Christians in the second century. It was written by a Christian named Aristides sometime before A.D. 150. It is one of the most compelling descriptions of Christian commitment and lifestyle found in the early church. As you read it, ask yourself, "What kind of home must have produced this kind of Christian commitment?"

   They do good to their enemies; and their wives . . . are pure as virgins and their daughters modest; and their men abstain from all unlawful wedlock and from all impurity. . . . As for their servants or handmaids, or their children if any of them have any, they persuade them to become Christians for the love that they have towards them; and when they have become so, they call them without distinction brethren. . . . And they walk in all humility and kindness; and falsehood is not found among them; and they love one another; and from the widows they do not turn away their countenance; and they rescue the orphan . . . ; and he who has gives to him who has not without grudging; and when they see the stranger they bring him to their dwellings and rejoice over him as over a true brother; for they do not call brothers those that are after the flesh but those who are in the spirit and in God; . . . and if they hear that any of their number is imprisoned or oppressed for the name of their Messiah all of them provide for his needs, and if it is possible that he may be delivered they deliver him. And if there is among them a man that is poor or needy and they have not an abundance of necessaries, they fast two or three days that they may supply the needy with their necessary food.

And they observe scrupulously the commandments of their Messiah; they live honestly and soberly, as the Lord their God commanded them. Every morning and at all hours on account of the goodnesses of God towards them they praise and laud him; and over their food and over their drink they render him thanks. . . .

. . . Such is the ordinance of the law of the Christians . . . , such their conduct. As men who know God they ask from him petitions which are proper for him to give and for them to receive; and thus they accomplish the course of their lives. And because they acknowledge the goodnesses of God towards them, lo! on account of them there flows forth the beauty that is in the world.
(*The Epistle to Diognetus,* ch. 5. See Cyril Richardson,

Early Christian Fathers [Philadelphia: The Westminster Press, 1963], pp. 216–218.)

a. Write down at least five behavior patterns of the early Christians which you think we should emulate today.

(1) ______________________________

(2) ______________________________

(3) ______________________________

(4) ______________________________

(5) ______________________________

b. What can you do in the home to transmit these values?

____

____

____

____

____

c. How can worship in the home relate to these values? Give specific examples. ______________________________

____

____

____

Practical Implications for Today

8. Worship in the heart. Read Deuteronomy 6:5.

What is the relationship of the heart to the home in Christian worship? What does this say to you? ______________

____

____

9. Worship in the home. Read Deuteronomy 6:20.

   How do you convey the *meaning* of the Christian faith in your home, and not just the facts?

10. Worship in the church. Read Ephesians 5:19.

    What is the connection between worship in your home and worship in the church?

    What steps do you need to take to improve the togetherness of the family as it worships in the local church?

11. Worship in the world. Read 1 Peter 2:9–10.

    How can you, through the witness of your home, "declare the praises of him who called you out of darkness into his wonderful light"? Jot down at least three specific ways to fulfill this calling. ________________

____

____

____

4

WORSHIP IN THE CHURCH

In the Christian tradition of worship, a strong emphasis has always been placed on the corporate body of Christ gathered together.

When God's people come together, the body of Christ comes alive as a corporate body with its many parts. For this reason, the personal intention of the believer, the involvement of the family, and the bringing of gifts within the service of worship are of utmost importance.

Public worship can never occur with only one person. That is private worship. One person alone does not represent the fullness and variety that is present in the body of Christ.

In this lesson, we are going to look at worship in the church and ask what gift(s) we can bring to the activity.

The Biblical Basis

1. Read Exodus 24:1–8. This is an account of the first service of public worship between God and His people, Israel.

   a. What general principles of public worship can be drawn from this account? ______________________

   ____

   ____

   ____

   b. What specific things do you find the lay person doing?

   ____

   ____

   c. Can you suggest some ways in which this account may inform and challenge your local church? ________

   ____

   ____

2. Read 2 Chronicles 29:3–6, 10–11, 16, 20, 27–31, 36. This is an account of the restoration of worship in Israel during the reign of Hezekiah.

   a. What does this passage say about the relationship between worship and renewal? ______________________

   ____

   ____

   ____

   ____

   b. According to the text, what may be involved in worship renewal? ______________________

____

____

____

c. What was the result of worship renewal in Hezekiah's time? ______________________________________

____

____

____

d. Suggest two implications of this text for worship renewal today. ______________________________________

____

____

3. Read Acts 2:42–47.

a. What were the essential features of worship in the early Christian community? ______________________________________

____

____

b. What were the results of this worship? ______________________________________

____

____

____

c. How does the worship described in this passage compare with the worship you experience in your local church? ______________________________________

4. Read 1 Corinthians 12:27–31.

   a. What is the point of this passage? ______

   b. What gift(s) do you bring to the worship of the local church? ______

The Experience of the Church

In the late medieval period, worship had been taken away from the people and put into the hands of the clergy and choir. Consequently worship became something to be watched and observed rather than something that was participated in. The genius of the Reformation was to put worship back into the hands of the people, to make worship congregational once again. Read the following quotations carefully, and consider the value of the principles they enunciate for worship in the church today.

5. Luther's recognition of the role Christian lay persons play in church and worship can be summarized as follows:

   —All Christians have the same standing before God. God makes no separation between clergy and laity.

—Each Christian has access to God through Jesus Christ. There is no need for a mediator other than Christ.

—Each Christian has access to the Word of God. The Word in its essential message is clear and can be understood by all.

—Each Christian has a responsibility to offer praise and obedience to God.

—Each Christian is responsible to hand down the gospel that he or she has received.

a. How does each of the above statements encourage you to be involved in the worship of your congregation? ______________________________

____

____

____

____

____

b. What specific things can you do in the worship of your church to fulfill your calling as a worshiper of God? ___

____

____

6. The following statement was written by a Catholic historian. It describes the commitment of Christians martyred during Queen Mary's reign in sixteenth-century England.

> Through their habitual frequentation of the Bible, these people have themselves become transformed into scriptural figures, and all the drama of their lives has itself

become transformed into a scriptural event, itself a continuation of the sacred story.

a. What does "the drama of their life has itself become transformed into a scriptural event" mean? ________

____

____

b. How does the above idea connect with your worship in the church? ________

____

____

Practical Implications for Today

7. Worship in the heart. Read Psalm 24:3–4.

Rewrite these verses in your own words. ________

____

____

____

____

What are some of the most beneficial ways you have personally prepared for public worship? ________

____

____

8. Worship in the home. Read Psalm 101:1–2.

What does it mean to walk within the house with a perfect heart? Give examples of what you have done or what you could do to fulfill that description. ________

____

____

____

9. Worship in the church. Review 2 Chronicles 29:5.

   If the word "rubbish" is analogous to that which the church must rid itself of before renewal can take place, then what might be rubbish in your church's worship service? ______________________________

   ____

   ____

   ____

10. Worship in the world. Read Colossians 3:15–17.

    What are some specific activities ("whatever you do in word or deed") in which you need to let "the peace of Christ rule in your heart"? ______________________________

    ____

    ____

    ____

    ____

5

WORSHIP IN THE WORLD

Most Christians readily acknowledge that worship occurs in the heart, the home, and the church. But when asked, "What does it mean to worship in the world," they frequently respond with a blank stare.

I know of a pastor who occasionally ends worship services by saying, "Worship has ended, the service has begun." This little play on words captures one of the aspects of worship in the world.

Worship is not only what we say with our lips, but also what we do with our lives. The worship of the church prepares us for what we need to do by putting us in contact with the Christian story, by renewing our vision of what we need to do. Thus worship, which begins in the heart and is expressed in the home and the church, extends to our lives in the world. Worship is all encompassing; it has to do with the whole of life. It is the inescapable dimension of our belonging to the Creator and Redeemer that is expressed by everything we do.

The Biblical Basis

1. Read Deuteronomy 15:7–11. This passage presents a portion of the covenant between God and Israel. The worship of God requires service that affects every aspect of life.

   a. Describe the attitude God expects Israel to display toward the poor. ____________________

   ____

   ____

   ____

   b. What is the result of not caring for the poor? __________

   ____

   ____

   ____

   c. What is the result of caring for the poor? __________

   ____

   ____

   ____

2. Read Amos 5:21–24. In this passage, Israel continues to go through the motions of worship but, at the same time, fails to care for the poor.

   a. What is one attitude of God's people toward the poor? See Amos 4:1; 5:11–12. ____________________

   ____

b. In your own words, describe the contrast between worship and justice that is set forth by Amos (5:21–24). ______

c. Do you really think God wants justice and not worship, or do you think this is a statement of Jewish irony? Explain. ______

d. What type of fruit should worship produce in our lives? ______

3. Read Matthew 5:3–12.

a. What does this passage suggest is the relationship between worship and poverty? ______

b. Who are the people described in this passage? ______

______

______

______

c. What insight into worship does your answer above provide? ______

______

______

______

4. Read Luke 4:16–19. This is the only account of a sermon preached by Jesus in a worshiping community.

   a. What does the Scripture passage Jesus read have to say about the relationship between worship and the poor?

   ______

   ______

   ______

   b. If He had developed His text more, what might have been the content of His sermon? ______

   ______

   ______

   ______

5. Read Acts 2:44–47. This account provides us with the earliest description of the Christian worshiping community.

   What seems to be the relationship between worship and poverty in this passage? ______

____

____

6. To what extent do you think Christians ought to be responsible for the needs of others? ______________

   Within the Christian community: ______________

   ____

   Outside the Christian community: ______________

   ____

The Experience of the Church

7. The following statement was written by Hippolytus in *The Apostolic Tradition* in A.D. 270. It shows the connection the early church made between worship and one's life in the world:

   > And when these things are completed, let each one hasten to do good works, and to please God and to live aright, devoting himself to the church, practicing the things he has learned, advancing in the service of God. (See Bard Thompson, *Liturgies of the Western Church* [New York: Meridian, 1961], p. 23.)

   a. Write down the phrases that connect worship and life in the world. ______________

      ____

      ____

   b. What have you done *this week* that relates to the worship of this past Sunday? Be specific. ______________

      ____

      ____

____

____

8. The following statement illustrates the many ways in which the Lord's Supper is connected with life and work in the world.

> In worship, the right relationship between God and his creation is manifested. The Eucharist shows us the utter dependence of all things on God, the adoration of God through the created order (as in the Sanctus), where through men's lips and by their lives they are ready to kneel in his presence, to sing his praise, and to offer to him their oblation of love and service. The created order is here doing what it is meant to do; for heaven and earth are united, living and departed are at one, and the creation is ordered for its own great good and for God's great glory. Man is in his place, nourished by the life that comes from God; he is man as God means him to be, the crown of the creation and the image and likeness of God himself. All that he does is related to God as he meets men in Christ and unites them with himself. Sin and failure are forgiven, strength is imparted, a redeemed and transfigured cosmos is both signified and present. Whenever the Body of Christ gathers its members for eucharistic worship, all this is seen, as men worship God the Father through Christ the Son in the power of the Holy Spirit. (Norman Pittenger, *Life as Eucharist* [Grand Rapids: Eerdmans, 1973], pp. 80–81.)

a. In the space below write down as many ideas as you can draw from the above statement that illustrate the relationship between worship and the world. ________

____

____

____

b. How many of these ideas were expressed in the most recent worship service of your church? ______________

____

____

Practical Implications for Today

9. Worship in the heart. Read Matthew 5:43–44. Meditate on the attitude that God works in the heart of a true worshiper toward the poor, the oppressed, and even those who may appear as enemies. How can you put this attitude to work in your life? ______________________

____

____

____

10. Worship in the home. Read Galatians 6:2. How does true worship in the home challenge us to care for the needs of those with whom we live? Give concrete suggestions. ______________________________

____

____

____

11. Worship in the church. Read Acts 4:32–37. To what extent does worship compel us to care for the needs of others in our immediate worshiping community? ________

____

____

Think of someone in need. What can your church do for that person or family? ______________________________

____

____

12. Worship in the world. Read James 1:27. List at least two specific ways to worship God based on this verse. ______

____

____

____

6

IN WORSHIP WE ACKNOWLEDGE GOD FOR WHO HE IS

The reason God created us is often forgotten—to worship Him. In Revelation, the worship book of the New Testament, John reminds us:

> You are worthy, our Lord and God,
> To receive glory and honor and power,
> For you created all things,
> and by your will they were created
> and have their being. (Revelation 4:11)

God is to be worshiped simply because of who He is. His character and being are such that they evoke the eternal praise of the celestial beings. How much more should we, mortal creatures who have been redeemed by His love, offer praise and adoration to His holy and majestic name? Remember, He, and He alone, is God.

The questions and exercises in this unit of study will help

us learn how to praise His name to His greater glory. Do them prayerfully.

The Biblical Basis

Read Isaiah 6:1–4 and Revelation 4:1–11. These passages emphasize praising God for His intrinsic value. Meditate on these verses and then answer the questions:

1. As you read these two descriptions of God, what two or three aspects of His character stand out to you? ________

    ____

    ____

    ____

2. These passages from Isaiah and Revelation are illustrations of heavenly worship. Do you think our worship here on earth ought to be patterned after heavenly worship? If so, how? ____________________

    ____

    ____

    ____

3. Do you think your church's worship service displays an adequate reverence for God? Why do you feel this way?

    ____

    ____

    ____

4. Read Exodus 26. How does this passage affirm the character of God as one of order and beauty? How can we worship the beauty and order of God today? ________

    ____

___

___

___

Worship is a meeting with God in which we praise and magnify Him for His goodness, His holiness, His majesty, and His beauty. In true worship, the worshiper is always affected by being in the presence of God Almighty. The following passages emphasize the impact worship has on us.

5. Read Exodus 19:16–25. This passage describes the effect the presence Holy God has on nature and humans. Write down the effect and attempt to interpret it in the lines below:

   a. The effect on nature — the interpretation

   ___ ___

   ___ ___

   ___ ___

   b. The effect on humans — the interpretation

   ___ ___

   ___ ___

   ___ ___

6. Read Exodus 34:29–35. What does this passage say about (a) God and (b) what it means to be in the presence of God?

   (a) ___

   (b) ___

7. Read Luke 9:28–36. What does this passage say about (a) God and (b) the effect of being in His presence?

(a) ____

(b) ____

____

The Experience of the Church

Throughout the church's history, God's people have expressed the majestic transcendence and worth of God through their hymns and prayers. Read and study the following hymn and prayer in a spirit of praise.

The gloria in excelsis Deo

(This hymn is based on Luke 2:14 and is found in the church as early as the third century.)

Glory be to God on high,
and on earth peace, good will towards men.

We praise thee, we bless thee,
we worship thee,
we glorify thee,
we give thanks to thee for thy great glory,
O Lord God, heavenly King, God the Father Almighty.

O Lord, the only-begotten Son, Jesus Christ;
O Lord God, Lamb of God, Son of the Father,
that takest away the sins of the world,
have mercy upon us.

Thou that takest away the sins of the world,
receive our prayer.
Thou that sittest at the right hand of God the Father,
have mercy upon us.

For thou only art holy;
thou only art the Lord;
thou only, O Christ,
with the Holy Ghost,
art most high in the glory of God the Father, Amen.

8. What does this hymn say about God the Father? ______

______

______

______

9. What does it say about God the Son? ______

______

______

______

10. What does it say about God the Holy Spirit? ______

______

______

______

11. State the specific ways in which this hymn evokes praise to God in your heart. ______

______

______

______

Prayer of St. John Chrysostom:

(This prayer was used by John Chrysostom in the church's worship in fourth-century Constantinople.)

> It is fitting and right to hymn you, (to bless you, to praise you,) to give you thanks, to worship you in all places of your dominion. For you are God, ineffable, inconceivable, invisible, incomprehensible, existing always and in the same way, you and your only-begotten Son and your Holy Spirit. You brought us out of not-being to being; and when we had fallen, you raised us up again; and did

not cease to do everything until you had brought us up to heaven, and granted us the kingdom that is to come. For all these things we give thanks to you and to your only-begotten Son and to your Holy Spirit, for all that we know and do not know, your seen and unseen benefits that have come upon us. We give you thanks also for this ministry; vouchsafe to receive it from our hands, even though thousands of archangels and ten thousands of angels stand before you, cherubim and seraphim, with six wings and many eyes, flying on high (aloud) singing the triumphal hymn (proclaiming, crying, and saying:) Holy (holy, holy, Lord of Sabaoth; heaven and earth are full of your glory. Hosanna in the highest. Blessed is he who comes in the name of the Lord. Hosanna in the highest).
(See R.C.D. Jasper and G. J. Cuming, *Prayers of the Eucharist: Early and Reformed* [New York: Oxford University Press, 1980], p. 89.)

12. In what ways does this prayer extol or praise God? ______

______

______

______

13. What does it express about the ministry of worship? ______

______

______

______

14. How do you feel about joining heavenly worship in your praise of God? ______

______

____

____

Practical Implications for Today

The following questions and exercises will help you acknowledge God in His transcendent majesty in the heart, the home, the church, and the world.

15. Worship in the heart. Read Ephesians 5:19. Singing and making melody in your heart is one of the chief ways to experience a truth about God. Choose a hymn, chorus, or spiritual song (either from memory or from a hymn book) and sing it to yourself frequently through the day. In the space below, write down the result. ____________

    ____

    ____

    ____

16. Worship in the home. Read 1 John 4:8. In family devotions sometime this week, create a time when family members can respond spontaneously to the greatness of God. Let each member of the family complete the following: I believe God is . . . (You may want to go on until there are no more ideas that quickly come to mind.) Now, write down the result of this experience. ____________________________

    ____

    ____

    ____

17. Worship in the church. Read Romans 11:33. This Sunday make special note of those parts of the service

that concentrate on proclaiming the transcendence and holiness of God. Summarize the specific content that accomplished that under the following headings:

a. Prayers ______________________________

b. Hymns ______________________________

c. Scripture ______________________________

d. Sermon ______________________________

e. Anthem ______________________________

18. Worship in the world. Read Romans 12:1. Our service to God in the world may be expressed in our home, at work, with our neighbors and friends. Can you think of a way you can acknowledge God's supreme majesty through something you say or do in these contexts? I will

    ____

    ____

    In the space below, comment on the result. ______________

    ____

    ____

    ____

7

IN WORSHIP WE SEE OURSELVES FOR WHAT WE ARE

An axiom, or truth, found in both the Old and New Testament could be stated something like this: "When we see God for who He is, we see ourselves for what we are."

In the last study, we looked at God in His majestic transcendence and holiness. In this session, our study brings us to a confrontation with ourselves as we stand in the presence of Almighty God.

The Biblical Basis

1. Read Isaiah 6:1–5. What did Isaiah experience about himself? ______________________________

____

____

2. Read Luke 18:9–14. What does this passage say about the proper approach to God in worship? ______________

____

____

____

3. Read Luke 1:50. Read this verse in the context of the Magnificat (Luke 1:46–54). What indications are there that Mary's attitude shows a worshiping spirit? __________

____

____

In both the Old and New Testaments, an awareness of sinfulness is present in the context of worship. In the presence of God's holiness, we become aware of our sin. But God has provided a mediator for sinful persons to bring them into the Holy of Holies, into the very presence of God Himself. Read and study the following passages to see how God has provided us with forgiveness of sin and access to Himself.

4. Review Isaiah 6:1–7. What was Isaiah's experience in worship after he recognized his sinful condition in verse 5? ____

____

____

5. Read Leviticus 16:1–34. Answer the following:

   a. How is God described in this passage (verses 1–4)? ___

   ____

   ____

b. How are humans described in this passage (verse 16)?

____

____

c. What is the significance of the goat for the sin offering (verses 8–10, 15–19)? ____________________

____

____

d. What is the significance of the scapegoat (verses 8–10, 21–22)? ____________________

____

____

e. Why is one sacrificed and one sent away? __________

____

____

6. Read Hebrews 9:6–28. Study and meditate on this passage and then answer the following questions:

a. What was the meaning of the tabernacle sacrifices (verses 7–9)? ____________________

____

b. What is required for the remission of sin (verse 22)? ____

____

c. What has Christ accomplished by the sacrifice of Himself (verses 14, 15, 26)? ____________________

____

____

____

The Experience of the Church

The church in worship has always expressed its sinfulness before Almighty God. Following are two examples. Study these prayers and enter into their spirit of humility and contrition.

Below is John Calvin's admonition given to his parishioners before taking Holy Communion.

> Therefore, in accordance with the exhortation of St. Paul, let each man prove and examine his conscience, to see whether he has truly repented of his faults, and is satisfied with himself, desiring to live henceforth a holy life and according to God. Above all, let each man see whether he puts his trust in the mercy of God, and seeks his salvation entirely in Jesus Christ; and whether, renouncing all hatred and rancour, he truly intends and resolves to live in peace and brotherly love with his neighbours.
>
> If we have this testimony in our hearts before God, let us have no doubt at all that he claims us for his children, and that the Lord Jesus Christ addresses his words to us, to invite us to his table, and to present us with this holy sacrament which he communicated to his disciples.
>
> And although we may feel within ourselves much frailty and misery from not having perfect faith, and from being inclined to unbelief and distrust, as well as from not being devoted to the service of God so entirely and with such zeal as we ought, and from having to war daily against the lusts of our flesh, nevertheless, since our Lord has graciously permitted us to have his gospel imprinted on our hearts, in order to withstand all unbelief, and has given us the desire and longing to renounce our own desires, in order to follow righteousness and his holy commandments, let us all be assured that the sins and imperfections which remain in us will not prevent him

> from receiving us, and making us worthy to partake of this spiritual table: for we do not come to declare that we are perfect or righteous in ourselves; but, on the contrary, by seeking our life in Christ, we confess that we are in death. Let us therefore understand that this sacrament is a medicine for the spiritually poor and sick, and that the only worthiness which our Saviour requires in us is to know ourselves, so as to be dissatisfied with our vices, and have all our pleasure, joy and contentment in him alone.
>
> John Calvin: Form of Church Prayers, Geneva 1542

7. Reflecting on Calvin's prayer, answer the following questions:

a. What is the purpose of the examination of conscience?

____

____

____

____

b. What is the attitude of the believer toward his or her sin? ________________________

____

____

____

c. What does the Savior require of us? ______________

____

____

____

From the Book of Common Prayer:

> Most merciful God
> We confess that we have sinned against you in thought, word, and deed,
> By what we have done, and by what we have left undone.
> We have not loved you with our whole heart;
> We have not loved our neighbors as ourselves.
> We are truly sorry and humbly repent.
> For the sake of your Son Jesus Christ,
> have mercy on us and forgive us;
> that we may delight in your will,
> and walk in your ways,
> To the glory of your name. Amen

8. Meditate on the above prayer and answer these questions:

   a. What attribute of God is addressed? ______________________

   ____

   b. What is the *extent* of the sin confessed? ______________________

   ____

   ____

   ____

   ____

   c. What is the resolve of the forgiven penitent? ______________

   ____

   ____

Practical Implications for Today

9. Read John 1:9. Personal confession is difficult because it requires self-examination. Take time to examine your

attitudes, your treatment of family and friends, your use of time, and your involvements. Write down those areas which you feel need confession. ______________________

____

____

____

____

10. Read Matthew 18:15. Sometimes it is in the home that we act the least Christian. Have you done something recently that offended another family member? Are you now alienated from another person in the family? Go make it right and record the experience in the space below. ______________________________________

    ____

    ____

    ____

    ____

11. Observe references to the human condition of sinfulness in church this Sunday. Record those references below:

    a. Prayers ______________________________________

    ____

    b. Scripture ____________________________________

    ____

    c. Hymns _______________________________________

    ____

    d. Other ____

    ____

12. Read Romans 7:20–25. What specific struggles do you have as you attempt to extend the worship experience in your daily work and life in the world? Write down these struggles and share them with others in your group. ____

    ____

    ____

    ____

    ____

8

IN WORSHIP WE HEAR THE GOOD NEWS

Someone once said that worship is "doing" the faith. That's a good point; in worship we tell and act out the story of the gospel.

In our preceding studies, we have told two important parts of the Christian story. We stood before God and acknowledged Him in His holiness and transcendence saying, "You are God; there is none beside You." That's where worship starts.

Then, we saw ourselves for what we were. In contrast to the holiness and majesty of God, we, like Isaiah, realized we were lost sinners. But thanks be to God, that's not the end of the Christian story.

A third part of the story, the one that we will cover in this lesson, is to hear the good news. God, the story tells us, has forgiven us in Jesus Christ. Our worship is not complete without hearing the word of forgiveness.

The Biblical Basis

The good-news side of worship is rooted in event, or history. Worship in the Old Testament is based on the promise of God to release His people from sin.

The exodus event was an important expression of that promise. In this event, God sent Moses to lead the people of Israel out of their Egyptian bondage. The escape from Egypt; the crossing of the Red Sea; and the covenant, or promise, made between God and Israel at Mt. Sinai is the content of this event.

Likewise, the New Covenant, the fulfillment of God's promise to release His people from sin, is rooted in an event. Christian worship always refers back to that cluster of occurrences, which we call the Christ-event. In this event, the Son of God was born of a virgin, lived among us, was crucified, buried, and rose from the grave. That is good news.

The following readings and questions are designed to help you get a better grasp of how the good news we celebrate is rooted in event.

1. Read Exodus 12:21–28, 42.

   a. To what historical event does this passage refer? ______

   ____

   ____

   b. Write down the verses that connect this event with worship. ______________________________

   ____

   ____

   c. Compare Exodus 12:21 with the following passages and write down the portion of the verse that reminds you of the event in the Old Testament.

John 1:29 ______________________________

Acts 8:32 ______________________________

1 Peter 1:19 ______________________________

1 Corinthians 5:7 ______________________________

2. Read Exodus 24:1–8. This passage describes the covenant made between God and Israel after the Exodus.

   a. What characterizes a covenant? ______________________________

   ____

   b. What does Israel agree to do? ______________________________

   ____

   c. What is the sign of the covenant in verse 8? ______________________________

   ____

   d. Compare this covenant with the New Covenant described in the book of Hebrews by writing down the essential teaching of each of the following verses.

   Hebrews 9:11–15 ______________________________

   ____

   ____

   Hebrews 9:16–20 ______________________________

   ____

   ____

3. Read Matthew 26:26–30.

   a. What event does this passage describe? ______________________________

   ____

b. Why has this event always been a part of worship? ____

____

____

c. In worship, different words have been used to describe this event. Look them up in the following passages, and note what experience each is describing.

Acts 2:42. ______________________________________

____

1 Corinthians 11:17–34. __________________________

____

1 Corinthians 10:16. _____________________________

____

1 Corinthians 14:16. _____________________________

____

4. Read Revelation 5:1–14. In this passage of heavenly worship, what reasons can you find for worshiping in verses 8–14? ____________________________________

____

____

____

____

The Experience of the Church

In the history of the church, the gospel has always stood at the center of worship. The church has concentrated on telling and acting out the story through words and the Supper. The following two examples are from the early church describing their worship. Read them and answer the questions below.

5. A second-century description of worship:

> And on the day called Sunday there is a meeting in one place of those who live in cities or the country, and the memoirs of the apostles or the writings of the prophets are read as long as time permits. When the reader has finished, the president in a discourse urges and invites [us] to the imitation of these noble things. Then we all stand up together and offer prayers. And, as said before, when we have finished the prayer, bread is brought, and wine and water, and the president similarly sends up prayers and thanksgivings to the best of his ability, and the congregation assents, saying the Amen; the distribution, and reception of the consecrated [elements] by each one, takes place and they are sent to the absent by the deacons.
> ("First Apology of Justin," ch. 67. See Cyril Richardson, *Early Christian Fathers* [Philadelphia: The Westminster Press, 1963], p. 287.)

a. Make an outline of this service. ______________________

____

____

____

____

____

b. Indicate those parts of the service in which you think the good news would be presented. ______________

____

____

6. An early third-century Eucharistic prayer (the prayer said at the Lord's Supper):

The Lord be with you.

And all shall say:

And with your spirit.
Up with your hearts.
We have them with the Lord.
Let us give thanks to the Lord.
It is fitting and right.

And then he shall continue thus:

We render thanks to you, O God, through your beloved child Jesus Christ, whom in the last times you sent to us as saviour and redeemer and angel of your will;

who is your inseparable Word, through whom you made all things, and in whom you were well pleased.

You sent him from heaven into the Virgin's womb; and, conceived in the womb, he was made flesh and was manifested as your Son, being born of the Holy Spirit and the Virgin.

Fulfilling your will and gaining for you a holy people, he stretched out his hands when he should suffer, that he might release from suffering those who have believed in you.

And when he was betrayed to voluntary suffering that he might destroy death, and break the bonds of the devil, and tread down hell, and shine upon the righteous, and fix the limit, and manifest the resurrection,

he took bread and gave thanks to you, saying, "Take, eat; this is my body, which shall be broken for you." Likewise also the cup, saying, "This is my blood, which is shed for you;

when you do this, you make my remembrance."

Remembering therefore his death and resurrection, we offer to you the bread and the cup, giving you thanks because you have held us worthy to stand before you and minister to you.

And we ask that you would send your Holy Spirit upon the offering of your holy Church; that, gathering them into one, you would grant to all who partake of the holy things (to partake) for the fullness of the Holy Spirit for the confirmation of faith in truth;

that we may praise and glorify you through your child Jesus Christ, through whom be glory and honour to you, to the Father and the Son with the Holy Spirit, in your holy Church, both now and to the ages of ages. (Amen.) (*The Apostolic Tradition of Hippolytus*. See Jasper and Cuming, *Eucharistic Prayers: Early and Reformed*, pp. 22–23.)

a. Read through this prayer carefully, and mark down the word or phrase in each section that you believe pertains to the good news.

1. ______
2. ______
3. ______
4. ______
5. ______
6. ______
7. ______
8. ______
9. ______
10. ______
11. ______
12. ______

13. ______________________________

7. How do both of these early Christian documents tell and act out the good news? ______________________________

____

____

____

____

Practical Implications for Today

Our study in both biblical and historical sources demonstrates that worship is rooted in an event—the birth, life, death, and resurrection of Christ. It is this event which distinguishes Christian worship from other forms of worship. Worship is more than a feeling, more than a sense of awe and reverence. Of course it is that, but it is that with reference to the God who has acted to release us from our bondage to evil. Thus, our worship in the heart, home, church, and world always brings the Christ-event and the good news of salvation to mind.

8. Worship in the heart. Read Romans 10:9. What does this verse require of you if you are to be a true worshiper of God? ______________________________

____

____

____

____

9. Worship in the home. Read Acts 16:25–34. According to this passage, what is the prerequisite for home worship? ______________________________

____

____

____

10. Worship in the church. Read Acts 2:42. How does this passage emphasize the good news in public worship? ___

    ____

    This next Sunday, pay careful attention to those aspects of morning worship that emphasize the good news. Write them below.

    Prayers ________________________________

    Hymns ________________________________

    Sermon ________________________________

    Eucharist _______________________________

11. Worship in the world. Read Romans 12:1–2. What do these verses have to say about the way you live the good news? ____________________________

    ____

    ____

    ____

12. Resolve some way to enhance your worship in one of the four above areas. Write it down. __________________

    ____

    ____

9

IN WORSHIP WE AFFIRM THAT GOD IS IN CONTROL

A few years ago a speaker in the Wheaton College chapel said, "Life is something that happens to you when you have other plans."

These words were spoken in a message on suffering. In the space of a few years, this speaker had lost his wife through sudden death, his teenage son had to be committed to a psychiatric hospital, and his daughter had gone through two divorces.

This man, a devoted disciple of Christ, told us how he had to learn that he was not in control of life. For him, living was not directing his own course so much as it was learning how to rest in the sovereignty of God.

Your life may also be filled with unexpected "intrusions," with things that happened to you when you had other plans.

In worship, the inexplicable and unwanted events of our life are put into perspective. For in worship we are met by

God, who assures us that He is in control. Our life is not a mere cork in the ocean, tossed about in the rage of a stormy sea. A loving and compassionate God is watching, guiding, and directing our path from day to day.

In our study this week, we let Scripture and the experience of the church tell us how others have sensed the protective and loving guidance of God.

The Biblical Basis

The following Scripture passages provide illustrations of people who have gone through hard times. Study these passages to see how they coped with their problems.

1. Read Genesis 50:15–21.

   a. Describe the background of this passage. What did the brothers of Joseph do that put them in such fear? ______

   ____

   ____

   b. What was Joseph's attitude? __________________

   ____

   ____

2. Read Exodus 6:1–8

   a. Describe the background of this passage. What is the physical situation and emotional condition of Israel? __

   ____

   ____

   ____

   b. How often does the phrase "I am the Lord" appear? Why do you suppose the Lord used this phrase so many times? ____________________

____

____

3. Read Joshua 1:1–9.

   a. What is the future of Israel (verse 2)? ______________

   ____

   b. What is Israel asked to do (verses 6–9)? ______________

   ____

   ____

   ____

   ____

   c. What are the promises of God? ______________

   ____

   ____

   ____

Now, in your mind and heart, go back over these three illustrations (Joseph, Israel in bondage, Israel at the Jordan) and create a description of God.

4. Write down the words, phrases, and images of God that come to mind. ______________

   ____

   ____

   ____

5. Read Matthew 28:20. Write down three words from this passage that hold the greatest comfort to you today. ____

6. Read Romans 8:28. Replace the words "all things" with two or three incidents in your life that happened when you had other plans. ______

The Experience of the Church

In both personal and corporate worship, the "God who is there" is made real to us. As you study the following selections from the Psalms and from prayers and hymns of the church, open yourself to Him who shows Himself a loving and compassionate God, in control of all things.

7. Read Psalm 136. This Psalm describes the historical experience of Israel. Write a six-line, "real life" psalm that goes through the events of your life. Can you add to each line, "His mercy endures forever"?

8. In prayer we acknowledge God's control over life. Study the following prayer of the church and answer the questions below.

With all our heart and with all our mind, let us pray to the Lord, saying, "Lord, have mercy."

For the peace from above, for the loving kindness of God, and for the salvation of our souls, let us pray to the Lord.
Lord, have mercy.

For the peace of the world, for the welfare of the holy Church of God, and for the unity of all peoples, let us pray to the Lord.
Lord, have mercy.

For our Bishop, and for all the clergy and people, let us pray to the Lord.
Lord, have mercy.

For our President, for the leaders of the nations, and for all in authority, let us pray to the Lord.
Lord, have mercy.

For this city (town, village, ____________________), for every city and community, and for those who live in them, let us pray to the Lord.
Lord, have mercy.

For seasonable weather, and for an abundance of the fruits of the earth, let us pray to the Lord.
Lord, have mercy.

For the good earth which God has given us, and for the wisdom and will to conserve it, let us pray to the Lord.
Lord, have mercy.

For those who travel on land, on water, or in the air (or through outer space), let us pray to the Lord.
Lord, have mercy.

For the aged and infirm, for the widowed and orphans, and for the sick and the suffering, let us pray to the Lord.
Lord, have mercy.

For ________________, let us pray to the Lord.
Lord, have mercy.

For the poor and the oppressed, for the unemployed and the destitute, for prisoners and captives, and for all who remember and care for them, let us pray to the Lord.
Lord, have mercy.

For all who have died in the hope of the resurrection, and for all the departed, let us pray to the Lord.
Lord, have mercy.

For deliverance from all danger, violence, oppression, and degradation, let us pray to the Lord.
Lord, have mercy.

For the absolution and remission of our sins and offenses, let us pray to the Lord.
Lord, have mercy.

That we may end our lives in faith and hope, without suffering and without reproach, let us pray to the Lord.
Lord, have mercy.

Defend us, deliver us, and in thy compassion protect us, O Lord, by thy grace.
Lord, have mercy.

The Book of Common Prayer

a. Go back through the prayer and underline all the people, places, and events over which God is in control.

b. In the space below, write down that person, place, or thing that you need to yield to God's control. ________

____

____

____

9. One of the ancient prayers of the church that is still used more than any other prayer in personal and corporate worship is the Lord's Prayer.

   Meditate on this prayer and respond to the following questions.

   Our Father, who art in heaven,
   hallowed be thy Name,
   thy kingdom come,
   thy will be done,
   on earth as it is in heaven.
   Give us this day our daily bread.
   And forgive us our trespasses,
   as we forgive those
   who trespass against us.
   And lead us not into temptation,
   but deliver us from evil.
   For thine is the kingdom,
   and the power, and the glory,
   forever and ever. Amen

   a. What are the implications of the phrase "our Father"?

   ____

   ____

   b. What are the implications of the phrase "thy will be done on earth as it is in heaven"? ________________

   ____

   ____

10. Hymns often express the care that God exercises over His people and bid the worshiper to cast his cares on

God. Write down the title of one hymn that has accomplished this for you. Describe the experience. ____

____

____

____

____

Practical Implications for Today

In this study, our concern is to emphasize God's sovereign and loving control over all of life. All the pains and triumphs of life can be lifted up to Him in worship, and through worship God gives us back our lives and assures us of His presence. Apply this principle now to your experience of worship in your heart, home, church, and life in the world.

11. Worship in the heart. Read Psalm 18:1–3. Choose one event from your life that continues to trouble you. Offer it to the Lord and trust Him to be your deliverer. Write it down. If it is too personal to describe, put "an unwritten offering." ________________________________

    ____

    ____

12. Worship in the home. Read Psalm 1:1–3. Insert the word "family" where it's appropriate. What specific change needs to occur so that God will be Lord of your home and you can be like a "tree planted by the rivers of water"? Write it down and offer it to the Lord. __________

    ____

    ____

____

____

13. Worship in church. Read Psalm 150. This Sunday in worship, pay special attention to the ways in which the various parts of the service acknowledge that God is in control and those parts that call the worshiper to cast all care on Him. Write them down.

    Prayers ________________________________

    Hymns ________________________________

    Scripture ______________________________

    Sermon _______________________________

    Other _________________________________

14. Worship in the world. Read Psalm 148. Is there any part of your life and work in the world that places you under special stress? Write it down as an offering to God. _____

    ____

    ____

10

IN WORSHIP WE EXPERIENCE THE BODY OF CHRIST

We've already established that worship is not done alone, even the worship of the heart. In worship we are always mysteriously connected with other Christians who are worshiping, whether they are here on earth or in heaven.

Worship belongs to the Body of Christ. Christ's Body is not a mere collection of individual Christians. Rather, the image of the Body is that of a being with many parts that are all interrelated. Just as an arm would not be able to sustain life apart from its attachment to the body, so we cannot express or enjoy spiritual life apart from our being connected to the whole Body of Christ.

Christ's Body is a community—a family. Our parents accepted us as living members of a physical family and gave us love, shelter, food, and clothing. They nurtured us into adulthood. So the church, our new family, accepts us into its membership, and feeds, sustains, and nourishes us into maturity.

It's in worship that we take our place alongside others, and with them as our brothers and sisters, we extol the Lord and minister to each other's needs.

In this study, our emphasis is on the experience of community that is achieved through our worship. Read and study the material carefully and apply it to your worship in the Body.

The Biblical Basis

Both the Old and New Testaments emphasize that God's people constitute a community. In the Old Testament, God spoke of Israel as "a people holy to the Lord your God. The Lord your God has chosen you out of all the peoples on the face of the earth to be his people, his treasured possession" (Deuteronomy 7:6). These same words are used by Peter in the New Testament to describe God's new people, the church. He writes, "You are a chosen people, a royal priesthood, a holy nation, a people belonging to God, that you may declare the praises of him who called you out of darkness into his wonderful light" (1 Peter 2:9). Note how Peter's emphasis is on the purpose of the people. They are to declare His praises! So, the purpose of the Body is to worship God—to praise Him. In the following material we will learn how to do this *together*.

1. Read 1 Corinthians 12:1–11.

   a. What is the point of this passage? ______________________

   ____

   ____

b. What is the purpose of having a gift? ______

______

______

c. What do you think your gift is? ______

______

______

2. Read 1 Corinthians 12:12–19.

a. Rephrase verse 12 in your own words. ______

______

______

b. What does verse 14 say to you about your relationship with other members of the Christian community? ______

______

______

c. What part of the local body are you? ______

______

______

3. Read 1 Corinthians 12:20–31.

a. A schism means an alienation between you and any other member of the body of Christ. How is a schism overcome? ______

______

Can you think of an example in your own life to which you might apply this truth? ______

______

b. Rewrite verse 26, using a current example of someone who has either suffered or received an honor. ________

____

____

4. What is "the most excellent way" described in 1 Corinthians 12:31? ________________________________

____

5. Read 1 Corinthians 13.

   a. List the features of love as described by Paul.

   ________________ ________________

   ________________ ________________

   ________________ ________________

   ________________ ________________

   b. Can you think of a situation that would improve if you were to live this way? Write it down. ____________

   ____

   ____

   ____

The Experience of the Church

Throughout history, many have written of the community nature of worship and of the glory of experiencing the body of Christ through worship. Here are three examples. Read them and answer the questions thoughtfully.

6. A writing from the second century:

   Wherefore your accord and harmonious love is a hymn to Jesus Christ. Yes, one and all, you should form

> yourselves into a choir, so that, in perfect harmony and taking your pitch from God, you may sing in unison and with one voice to the Father through Jesus Christ. Thus he will heed you, and by your good deeds he will recognize you are members of his Son. Therefore you need to abide in irreproachable unity if you really want to be God's members forever.
>
> If in so short a time I could get so close to your bishop—I do not mean in a natural way, but in a spiritual—how much more do I congratulate you on having such intimacy with him as the Church enjoys with Jesus Christ, and Jesus Christ with the Father. That is how unity and harmony come to prevail everywhere. Make no mistake about it. If anyone is not inside the sanctuary, he lacks God's bread. And if the prayer of one or two has great avail, how much more that of the bishop and the total Church. He who fails to join in your worship shows his arrogance by the very fact of becoming a schismatic. ("Ignatius, Letter to the Epheshians." See Cyril Richardson, *Early Christian Fathers*, p. 89.)

a. What image does Ignatius use to describe the unity of the church? ______________________________

____

b. Can you think of other images that express the same idea? ______________________________

____

____

c. What can you do in your local church to help attain this ideal? ______________________________

____

____

____

7. A writing from an evangelical leader:

> Yet to worship with God's people in the church is not optional but imperative, and watching TV services is, except perhaps for "shut-ins," no substitute. We worship God not because we feel like it, but because He is God and worship is His due and our necessity.
>
> Frank Gaebelein

a. Is there a danger to TV Christianity? If so, what is it? ___

____

____

b. Is it possible to practice a TV-type Christianity even though attending a local church? If so, how? ________

____

____

____

8. A writing from a twentieth-century theologian:

> The early Christians thus understood the deep meaning of the symbol instituted by Jesus. Its social impact was the main criterion of its value and credibility. That is why the early Christians were so acceptable to many, especially the poor, and so detested by some of the powerful, particularly the exploiters. Christianity was then a dynamic movement of human liberation from selfishness and exploitation. All were to be equal in the believing community and this was symbolized by the eucharistic meal.

(Tissa Balasuriya, *The Eucharist and Human Liberation* [New York: Orbis, 1979], p. 25.)

What can you do today that will express what Balasuriya is saying? ______________________________

____

____

____

Practical Implications for Today

The concern of this study is to demonstrate that when we worship we do not worship alone. We belong to a worshiping community. For that reason, we are to bring our gift(s) to that community for the good of all. But equally, when we worship in community with others, we receive the benefit of those gifts which are brought by others. Apply this principle to your life as you think about your worship in heart, home, church, and world.

9. Worship in the heart. Read Hebrews 13:1. Worship begins in the heart that is characterized by love. Examine your heart and ask, "Do I truly love God and my fellow man?" Write down the result of your self-examination. __

   ____

   ____

   ____

10. Worship in the home. Read Hebrews 13:2–3. Worship has to do with relationships. Write down the strongest and weakest relationships currently in your home, and determine how you will strengthen the weaker ones.

HELPS FOR LEADERS

STUDY ONE: WORSHIP IS SOMETHING WE DO

Focus

The primary focus of this study is on worship as a verb, not a noun. You will want to emphasize this in your opening remarks. Then you may ask the following questions to help each person identify the issue with real life examples.

1. Give an example of a worship service that treated worship as a noun. (For example, you were a passive observer; you were worshiping in your heart, but apart from singing, you were not an active participant; worship was being done to you or for you.)
2. Give an example of a worship service in which worship was regarded as a verb. (For example, you were an active participant; you were doing the worshiping.)

The Biblical Basis

Emphasize the fact that our perception of God centers around His character and His works. We worship Him because He is holy, righteous, sovereign, almighty, etc. We also worship Him because of the great deeds He has done for us.

Questions 1–3. These verses emphasize the character of God. Ask (1), "What specific ways do our actions fail to show an awe and reverence for the majesty of God?" and (2), "What can we do to acknowledge God's majesty?"

Questions 4–6. These passages emphasize worshiping God for what He has done. Specifically in worship we center on: (1) He created us (Q 4); (2) He redeemed us (Q 5); and (3) He has brought us together into a covenant community—the church (Q 6). Ask, "What difference would it make in our lives if we lived in constant awareness of these three realms of thankfulness?"

The Experience of the Church

This material gives specific examples of how Christians have given thanks to God for His person and work. After reviewing the answers to the questions, ask, "How can you find ways in your life and work to give continual thanks to God for His person and work?"

Practical Implications for Today

Your concern here is to get each individual within the group to make a commitment to be more deeply involved in worship in her heart, home, church, and life in the world. Ask each person to make a concerted effort during the week to be conscious of how she worships in each of these areas. Suggest that she concentrate on one area in which to institute one new idea in the upcoming week. You may want to take time in your next session for several reports.

STUDY TWO: WORSHIP IN THE HEART

Warmup: Begin the study by asking a few women to report on their worship experiences since the last session. It might be wise to limit each report to three to five minutes.

Focus

This study focuses on each member's personal relationship with Jesus Christ. Stress the need for the heart to be turned away from sin toward Jesus Christ. Heart conversion to Jesus Christ is expressed in the adoption of a Christian view of the world, a commitment to a Christian value system, a relationship with the people of God, a concern to grow in the faith, and a love for the church. You might give a brief (five-minute) but specific testimony on how God has affected one of those areas or ask another member of the group to do so. (A few minutes advance notice to prepare would be appreciated by that person.)

The Biblical Basis

These biblical passages provide specific examples of the heart attitude we need in order to come before God. The sinner is to be characterized by a broken spirit (Job Q 1–2; Mary Q 3). The emphasis of Jesus' words is that those who come to Him do so out of need and are not acting as persons who have control of their destinies (Q 4). The Pauline description of Jesus' attitude gives us the model of how we are to come to God (Q 5). As Christ came to us without pretension, so we are to come to the Father. We must set aside all our hopes for worldly ambition and all our beliefs in our capability to save ourselves. We must trust in God alone, coming to Him through Christ in humility of spirit.

Experience of the Church

This section gives an example of how seriously Christians have taken the calling to worship God in the heart. The heart, one might say, must be a cleansed vessel if it is to worship God fully. Self-examination and personal confession prepares the heart to worship (Q 7). The Jesus Prayer (Q 8) is one way of keeping your heart conscious of Him. Ask, (1) "Have you used either of these methods to keep Jesus in your heart?"; (2) "Comment on the results of this method"; and (3) "What other ways have you found that keep Jesus before you?"

Practical Implications for Today

As in last week's lesson, you want each individual to practice worship before you meet again. Ask everyone to practice worship in the *heart* this week. Urge each person to concentrate on her awareness of worship and to be prepared to express the results to the group at the next meeting.

STUDY THREE: WORSHIP IN THE HOME

Warmup: Bring sheets of paper to class and ask the women to draw some way in which their experience of worshiping in the heart last week affected their lives. They might draw a scene in their homes or a mental image that often occurred during the week or a symbol of how they felt. Have the women share their drawings with the person on either side of them.

Focus

This study centers on the study of worship in the home and family. Stress that the family is the basic social unit of the church. Thus, a strong church derives from family and home units whose worship feeds into the worship of the church.

Begin by relating an incident or two from your own experience (or that of another) with family worship. Do not be afraid to express your failure. Most Christian families have great difficulty with family worship. An honest statement about your problems with family worship will put everyone at ease and allow you to discuss this issue in a candid and more helpful way.

The Biblical Basis

Home worship is seldom discussed in Scripture, but there are enough examples to give us a sense of its purposes. The Bible emphasizes that home worship centers around an explanation and celebration of historical events (in the Old Testament, the promised coming of a Savior, prefigured in the Exodus; in the New Testament, the Christ event) (Q 1). Home worship is also the context in which truth is passed down from generation to generation (Q 2 and 3). As Christians, we mustn't ignore the impact which worship in the home makes on the child (Q 4, 5, and 6). Stress the fact that faith is nourished and passed down in the home. Ask for examples.

The Experience of the Church

This section gives a specific example of home worship from the past. Note how home worship made an impact on the character and development of the Christian and then found expression in the society. After reviewing the answers to question 7, ask, "How can home worship be a solution to secularism today?"

Practical Implications for Today

This section puts into practice the principles you have learned about worship in the home.

First, work through questions 8–11, asking for examples and illustrations.

Next, talk about putting worship into practice in the home. Once again ask the students to make some resolves about their worship for the coming week.

STUDY FOUR: WORSHIP IN THE CHURCH

Warmup: Ask the women to comment on this statement: "Everything in a church service should be geared to the sermon. All else is preliminary or designed to close the service after the sermon."

Focus

This study helps you understand what you do in worship on Sunday morning. Ask the women to explain the focal point of the corporate worship of their churches. If you have women from a variety of traditions, this will prove to be an exciting exchange. If most of the women are from the same church background, you will want to allow less time for this section.

The Biblical Basis

This biblical study sets forth the basic ingredients of worship (Q 1), the importance of worship in renewal (Q 2), and the experience of worship in the early church (Q 3 and 4). In question 1, emphasize the following points from Exodus 24:1–8: (1) God calls us together in worship; (2) there is a structure of responsibility (not everyone plays the same part); (3) the Word is central; (4) the response of the people is necessary; and (5) worship occurs through an act of ratification (in the New Testament, it is the Lord's Supper).

The Experience of the Church

In this section, you will want to emphasize the importance of congregational involvement. Let's not be passive worshipers. Let's find ways to respond to God and to each other!

Practical Implications for Today

In this part of your discussion, concentrate on question 9. Emphasize the need to understand and feel what is done in worship. Encourage each person to come up with suggestions that will help her become more involved in the action of Sunday morning worship.

STUDY FIVE: WORSHIP IN THE WORLD

Warmup: Break the ice by asking several women to report on the way in which the last study helped them to understand the meaning of Sunday's service.

Focus

This study emphasizes that worship never ends. Its effects keep emanating farther out, like a pebble thrown in a pond causes ripples that keep going farther out. Worship in the heart, the home, and the church prepares us to serve in the world. Ask for an illustration of something that occurred to one of the class members in private, family, or corporate worship that affected a relationship, work, or life in some way.

The Biblical Basis

These passages focus on the relationship between worship and our concern for the poor of the world. You may want to cover questions 1–5 quickly and concentrate on question 6.

The Experience of the Church

These illustrations show that the church has always made a connection between worship and service. Concentrate on question 8 and the image of the Eucharist (Lord's Supper). The answers to a and b should provoke quite a discussion.

Practical Implications for Today

Concentrate on question 12 and ask each woman to make a resolve to fulfill in the near future.

STUDY SIX: IN WORSHIP WE ACKNOWLEDGE GOD FOR WHO HE IS

Warmup: Ask several women: "What aspect of God's character is most meaningful to you—His love, mercy, justice, holiness, or morality? Why?"

Focus

In the last four sessions, emphasis was placed on the four areas of worship: the heart, the home, the church, and the world. In this lesson, the emphasis shifts toward specific principles that will enhance worship in the heart, home, church, and world. Explain this shift.

The first principle, covered in this lesson, is that God is to be worshiped simply because He is God.

The Biblical Basis

These passages help each person face the need for awe and reverence in worship. God is transcendent. He is above and beyond His creation in that He is the sovereign Lord, King of the universe. Ask, "Do we really acknowledge God in all His majesty or have we overfamiliarized Him?" Keep this question before the group as you go through this section.

The Experience of the Church

Here are two examples of how God is acknowledged. Choose either.

Practical Implications for Today

Your emphasis should now shift to *how* to acknowledge God in heart, home, church, and life in the world. Stress practical application as you go through questions 15–18 and ask each woman to make a resolve she really can accomplish in each area.

STUDY SEVEN: IN WORSHIP WE SEE OURSELVES FOR WHAT WE ARE

Warmup: Get things going by asking several women to tell how they put the principle of acknowledging God in His majesty to work since the last session.

Focus

Emphasize that when we see God for who He is, we see ourselves for what we are. Is this not a principle of life? Do we not compare ourselves with others—looks, intelligence, ability, personality, etc.? Ought we not to concentrate on ourselves in relation to God?

The Biblical Basis

As you go through each of these questions, you will want to emphasize how God's holiness shows up our sinfulness and need of a Savior. Don't leave the group in despair. Emphasize, especially through questions 5 and 6, how God has provided a mediator and grants us forgiveness of sin.

The Experience of the Church

Choose to discuss one of these two examples of confession as we worship. Stress the need to acknowledge our sin whenever we come before the Lord.

Practical Implications for Today

Go through each of the questions, emphasizing the need to acknowledge and confess personal sin. Emphasize that confession makes us feel right toward ourselves, our family, the members of our church, and our neighbors. Ask each woman to concentrate on confession in each of these areas between now and the next session.

STUDY EIGHT: IN WORSHIP WE HEAR THE GOOD NEWS

Warmup: Ask if any of the women have visited a Jewish worship service. What was the focal point of it? If no one has, ask them what they think the focal point would be. (The group will discuss this today—it's the good news of God's provision, symbolized by the Exodus. But don't tell the group now; wait until you reach the biblical portion of the study.)

Focus

In this study, the third principle that in worship we hear the good news is the focal point of discussion. Emphasize how this theme relates to the two previous themes: When we (1) acknowledge God for who He is and (2) see ourselves for what we are, God gives us grace and forgiveness. That is the good news of both the Scripture and the Lord's Supper (Eucharist).

The Biblical Basis

These biblical passages demonstrate that worship relates to an event in history. Jewish worship is rooted in God's deliverance from the Pharaoh. That event prefigures Christian worship in which our deliverance from Satan and his hold over our lives is celebrated. Thus, the Christ-event is enacted in both the reading and preaching of the Word and in the acting out of that event in the Lord's Supper (Eucharist). Emphasize the importance of this event.

The Experience of the Church

As you go through these readings, emphasize the twofold structure of worship that revolves around: (a) the Word and (b) the Eucharist. The one tells the Christ story. The other acts it out. We need both.

Practical Implications for Today

As you work your way through questions 8–11, emphasize the need to keep the historic event of Jesus born, crucified, buried, and risen as central in all places of worship. Ask for resolves that concentrate on the grace of God expressed in the Christ-event.

STUDY NINE: IN WORSHIP WE AFFIRM THAT GOD IS IN CONTROL

Warmup: Open up the meeting by asking what impact concentrating on the Christ-event made: "Did it make a difference in your worship?"

Focus

This study affirms the loving and watchful care that God exercises over our lives. Worship, it should be emphasized, is all encompassing. It's not something that is unrelated to our day-today existence, to our joys and sufferings. In this lesson, we connect worship to the difficulties of life by affirming that God is in control.

The Biblical Basis

These passages help the women connect with God's people who have gone through trouble but who have found that God was always there. Go through each question, allowing the most time for question 6.

The Experience of the Church

Concentrate on the Psalm or one of the prayers. Go through it carefully, noting the specific troubles mentioned and talk about how God is always present with us in times of despair and grief.

Practical Implications for Today

Go through each question, keeping before the group that God is in control. Ask each woman to resolve this next week to apply that principle to her worship in heart, home, church, and world.

STUDY TEN: IN WORSHIP WE EXPERIENCE THE BODY OF CHRIST

Warmup: Begin with one or two testimonies as to how the truth that God is in control was of help in the experience of worship since the last session.

Focus

This study focuses on worship as a communal action. We don't just worship alone, but we also worship as a body. Stress the notion of our interrelatedness.

The Biblical Basis

After you have discussed each of these questions, bring the discussion back to question 2c. Encourage each person to name the gift that she can offer to the Body of Christ.

The Experience of the Church

Discuss each of these quotes, emphasizing the need to recognize what it means to be the Body of Christ.

Practical Implications for Today

Concentrate on the gift of love that Paul calls the highest gift. Ask, "How may the gift of love change the heart, the home, the church, and the world?"